Introduction

1991 was a special year for Dundee, as the City had its 800th birthday. This book was part of the Dundee 800 celebrations.

Like many people in Dundee I had heard about the whale, but not about the elephant. Both are fascinating historical facts and have instant appeal for children.

This was certainly the case when I went to Craigiebarns Primary School, Dundee to tell them the stories of the elephant and the whale. The delightful paintings in the book are a response to these stories.

This book was initiated by The Visual Arts Committee of Dundee 800. I acknowledge with thanks the help and assistance of Ethel Sharpe, Head Mistress, Moira Jarvis and the staff of Craigiebarns Primary School, Carolyn Bain, Janet Macdonald, Andy McKinlay and Bob Stewart of Central Media Service, and Allen Mackenzie, University of Dundee, Sandy Wilkie, Station Manager, Radio Tay and Jo Urquhart of Dundee 800.

My special thanks to Stuart Clumpas on behalf of Bar Chevrolet, Fat Sam's and Dance Factory Concerts and Printers Inglis Allen for their sponsorship and especially to Henny King, Director Dundee 800 for her enthusiasm and unflagging support in enabling this book to be published.

Augusta Hamlin

The Elephant
and
The Whale

Dundee 1706

Two stories about two
very unusual events.

One about the
largest land animal
and one about the
largest sea animal.

Both came to Dundee.

The elephant in 1706 and the
whale in 1883.

The first story is about the elephant.

  4

Three hundred years ago, not many people had seen an elephant or even heard about one. The Town Crier had been telling folk about this strange beast for weeks and weeks. It was hard for them to imagine it. Huge and grey, with a long trunk that looked like a snake, big ears that flapped like bird's wings, thick legs like tree trunks and a thin small tail. He could be very dangerous, for, if he felt like it, he could knock down walls, pick up people with his trunk and even crush them to death with his feet. The folk were fascinated and the children frightened, but all were determined to see him.

The Town Crier said the elephant would be coming to Dundee on April 26th, 1706.

The ele ele ele phant,
Is coming to Dundee,
Hurrah Hurrah Hurrah
What fun it's going to be.

The people of Dundee talked about nothing else and their children made up stories and games about him. The excitement grew and grew and the people got more and more frightened. They even imagined seeing the elephant around every corner and at night the children dreamt about him.

strange creatures with spots and stripes - squares and squiggles

-elephants in their dreams - fat and small - *elephants in their dreams* -

square and oval - elephants in their dreams - **fierce** and timid -

elephants in their dreams - elephants in their dreams -

ᴛᴜᴃᴃʏ and skinny - elephants in their dreams - big and little -

elephants in their dreams - strange creatures with spots and stripes -

squares and squiggles -*elephants in their dreams - fat and small -*

elephants in their dreams - **square and oval** - *elephants in their*

dreams - **fierce** and timid - *elephants in their dreams* - round and

flat - elephants in their dreams - ᴛᴜᴃᴃʏ and skinny - *elephants in their*

dreams - elephants in their dreams - strange creatures

with spots and stripes - squares and squiggles - *elephants in their*

dreams - fat and small - *elephants in their dreams* - **square and**

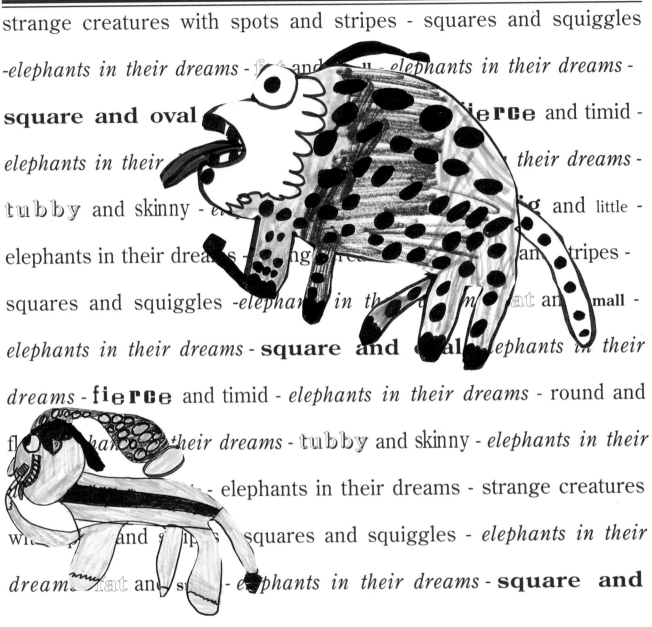

strange creatures with spots and stripes - squares and squiggles -elephants in their dreams - fat and small - elephants in their dreams - scaly and smooth - elephants in their dreams - fierce and timid - elephants in their dreams - round and flat - elephants in their dreams - tubby and skinny - elephants in their dreams - **big** and little - elephants in their dreams - strange creatures with spots and stripes - squares and squiggles - elephants in their dreams - fat and small - elephants in their dreams - round and oval - elephants in their dreams - **fierce** and timid - elephants in their dreams - round and flat - elephants in their dreams - tubby and skinny - elephants in their dreams - **big** and little - elephants in their dreams - strange creatures with spots and stripes - squares and squiggles - big and little

Can this be the elephant ? ? ?

  7

On April 25th, 1706, some children who had talked and dreamt
about the elephant could wait no longer.

"Let's go and find it", said Jimmy,
"Yes" said Janet,
"Yes" said Lizzie,
"Yes" said Pat.
"No" said wee Eddy, "I'm afraid, but don't leave me behind.
I want to come too." "Hurry up" they said for,

The ele ele ele phant,
Is coming to Dundee,
Hurrah Hurrah Hurrah
What fun it's going to be.

Off they went, across the fields and over the hills, puffing
and blowing, laughing and singing.

And suddenly, before them, they saw the most extraordinary sight.

  9

Jugglers, musicians,
Men on Stilts,
Fat ladies, Thin ladies,
Men in kilts,
All coming to Dundee.

And there, before their eyes, was this big, big beast, trunk swinging, ears flapping and with feet big enough to crush people.

"I'm off" said wee Eddy, "I'm afraid". "So am I" said Janet. "So am I" said Lizzie. "So am I" said Pat, "Let's go home."

Off they went, across the field and over the hills, puffing and blowing, and very frightened.

  11

  12

Next morning was hot.   The children, their fears forgotten, were
longing to see the elephant again. Hundreds of other folk were
longing to see the elephant too. The great day had arrived and the
people of Dundee were determined to make the most of it.
Off they went, across the field and over the hills, puffing and
blowing, laughing and singing

The ele ele ele phant,
Is coming to Dundee,
Hurrah Hurrah Hurrah
What fun it's going to be.

But suddenly, before them, they saw the most extraordinary sight.

Jugglers, musicians,
Men on Stilts,
Fat ladies, Thin ladies,
Men in kilts,
All coming to Dundee.

But they weren't laughing, they were crying, for the elephant
they had all been waiting to see had died in the night.

The ele ele ele phant
who almost came
to Dundee.
Such a pity for this
was not to be.

The poor elephant, who had been walking for many days, had got very tired and collapsed. The jugglers, musicians and men in kilts, had built a ditch so that he could lean against it but, unfortunately, it had rained in the night, the ditch had filled with water and the elephant had died of cold.

  16

But all was not lost, for in Dundee, at that time, was a famous doctor called Patrick Blair - a man with a very enquiring mind.
He knew about elephants and he also knew that he could learn a lot more if he could dissect the elephant.

He obtained permission from the Provost and set to work on that day in April 1706.

It was very hot and the smell was terrible but Dr Blair worked for many hours making notes and diagrams of the elephant.

From these notes, he wrote the famous book so that many, many people could read about this elephant for hundreds of years to come.

The second story is about the whale.

One day in December 1883, a huge whale visited Dundee.
The folk had heard about whales but not many had seen one.
And now there was one in the Tay.

The children came running out of their houses
Laughing and singing,
Round the corners,
Over the cobbles and to the water's edge.

For several days
he played
in the Tay,
eating all the
fish he could.

But the fishermen
met and talked
together about
the valuable prize
they had under
their noses.

They left mending their nets and cleaning their boats
to run over the cobbles to the water's edge.
And as they ran, they grabbed their harpoons and
launched their boats on the Tay.

  22

The Whale was angry and sore and he lashed out his tail at the fishermen. Great showers of water fell on the boats, wetting them all. The more the whale shook his tail, the more the fishermen were determined to catch it. They sang as they went after the poor creature,

No icy waters, no seas to sail;   God has provided us with a whale.

But suddenly all was quiet, the whale just disappeared and the fishermen had to go home disappointed.

The fishermen thought they would never see the whale again. But then the most extraordinary thing happened. A few days later the whale was sighted off Stonehaven, a poor weak creature with no fight left in him. Now the fishermen knew they had an easy catch.

They left mending their nets and cleaning their boats to run over the cobbles to the water's edge. They didn't need their harpoons this time, just two ropes to tie round his tail. It was so easy to bring in their huge catch.

The whale lay on the shore in Stonehaven. A rich prize for the poor fishermen.   They laughed and sang,

No icy waters, no sea to sail,
God really had provided them with a whale.

The fishermen clapped and cheered, for a man who came from Dundee bought the whale for two hundred and twenty six pounds. A lot of money in those days. He took the whale back to Dundee and now the skeleton hangs in the Museum in Barrack Street for all to see.

The whale who dared to come to Dundee

The Artists

Craigiebarns Primary School, Dundee celebrated its 21st birthday in the year of Dundee 800. It was founded in August 1970 and has established a fine reputation as a place of learning. "The Elephant and The Whale" paintings are part of the expressive arts which create an atmosphere in the school where the children learn in a happy, secure and stimulating environment.

The seven and eight year old artists were:

Class IIIA	Class IIIB
Sandra Mitchell	Katey Fotheringham
Andrew Clark	Alison Christie
Hilary Clark	Alexa Mills
Crawford Coutts	Brian Moore
Rosalind Morgan	Fergus Neville
Rachel Brand	Scott Stevenson
Helen Barclay	